The Queen Elizabeth Family

The Family Series

To my little princess Elizabeth
Victoria and her brave mum Anastassia
A. B.

EGMONT
We bring stories to life

Cover and interior illustrations by Aleksei Bitskoff

Text first published in Great Britain 1951
This edition published in 2018
by Egmont UK Limited
The Yellow Building, 1 Nicholas Road, London W11 4AN

Enid Blyton ®
Enid Blyton's signature is a Registered Trademark of Hodder and Stoughton Limited
Text copyright © Hodder and Stoughton Limited
Illustrations copyright © Hodder and Stoughton Limited

ISBN 978 1 4052 8952 8

www.egmont.co.uk

A CIP catalogue record for this title is available from the British Library

Printed and bound in Great Britain by the CPI Group

68505/1

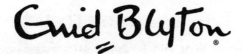

The Queen Elizabeth Family

The Family Series

EGMONT

CHAPTER ONE
Home for the Weekend

'Cuckoo!' called Belinda, Mike and Ann, as they opened the gate leading into a field.

'Cuckoo!' called back their mother, waving to them from the steps of one of the colourful caravans there. 'So glad you're back again!'

It was Friday afternoon. Mike, Belinda and Ann went to board at school all the week – but they came back to their caravan homes for the weekend. How they liked that!

'It's such fun to have school-life from Mondays to Fridays – and then home-life in our caravans from Fridays to Mondays,' said Belinda, as they walked over to the two pretty caravans. Then Ann ran on in front and hugged her mother.

'Mummy – I was top in writing!' she said.

'And I got one of my drawings pinned up on the wall,' said Belinda, proudly. 'I couldn't bring it home because it's got to stay there all next week.'

'And what about you, Mike?' asked his mother.

Mike grinned. 'Oh – I shot three goals yesterday afternoon,' he said. 'So our side won.'

'What a very successful week!' said Mummy, and she sounded pleased. 'Well – I expect you'd like to know what I've done too. I've made new curtains for your caravan – and I've made some lovely blackberry jelly!'

'Top marks, Mummy!' said Mike, and hugged her. 'Are we having the jelly for tea?'

'We are,' said his mother, and led the way into her caravan. There was one caravan for her and Daddy and one for the three children. Mummy had laid tea in her caravan, and it looked lovely. Blackberry jelly, cream in a little jug, new bread and butter, ginger biscuits, a chocolate cake and tiny buns made by their mother.

'Nicest tea in the world,' said Mike, and sat down at once.

'You must go and wash your hands,' said Ann. 'Just look at them!'

'My hands are clean, and anyway I only go if Mummy tells me,' said Mike at once. 'Wash your own!'

'Where's Daddy?' asked Belinda. 'Will he be late or early?'

'Late,' said Mummy. 'His firm is doing a lot of business with America just now, and he has to have a good many meetings with the men who are going over there.'

'I wish *we* could go to America,' said Belinda. 'We're learning about it in geography. Did you know you had to cross an enormous ocean called the Atlantic, Mummy, to get to America?'

'Well, yes, I did happen to know that,' said Mummy, pouring out mugs of milk.

'And did you know that there are two great ships called the *Queen Elizabeth* and the *Queen Mary*, that go across it in just a few days?' asked Ann. 'Goodness, how I'd like to go in one. They're supposed to be the finest ships in the world.'

'They are,' said Mummy. 'Well, perhaps one day we will all go to America, and you'll see what it's like.'

'Only if we could come back afterwards,' said Mike suddenly. 'I expect I'd like America very much – but I should always, always like England best.'

'Well, of course,' said Mummy. 'All the same you'd be astonished to see the food the Americans have – much better than ours!'

'But I don't think there could be a nicer tea than this,' said Ann at once, with her mouth full of bread and butter and blackberry jelly and cream.

Mummy laughed. 'Well, so long as you're satisfied, that's all right. Now – save some of the cream for Daddy. I've made him a blackberry tart for his supper, and he likes to pour cream all over it!'

'He'll get fat,' said Belinda. 'Why – here he is!'

And sure enough, there he was, coming in at the field-gate, waving to his little family, who were now crowding out of the caravan to meet him.

'Daddy!' yelled Ann, and almost fell down the steps. Mike reached him first. Daddy always liked his Friday welcome. He said he felt such an important person when four people rushed at top speed to meet him!

'Why are you home early?' asked Mike. 'Mummy said you'd be late.'

'I'm home early for a very important reason,' said Daddy. 'I've got an invitation for you all to see the *Queen Elizabeth* tomorrow! She's at Southampton, and sails on Saturday night. How would you like to have tea on board?'

'Daddy! *Really*?'

'Oh, how super!'

'It can't be true!'

Everyone spoke at once, and Daddy put his hands over his ears. 'Good gracious, I shall be deaf. It really *is* true. Look – here are the cards. We get on board with these, and we can see over quite a lot of the ship – and have tea on board too.'

'Did you say tomorrow?' said Mummy. 'That will be *lovely*! What a good thing it's Saturday and the children are home. It would have been so disappointing if it had been on a school-day. How are we going?'

'I rang up Granny and she's lending us her car,' said Daddy. 'She wants to come too. So do you think you could take Ann on your knee in front, Mummy, and let Granny go behind with Mike and Belinda.'

'Oh, easily,' said Mummy. 'It would be lovely to have Granny too. What a treat! The children will hardly believe a ship can be as big as the *Queen Elizabeth*!'

'I shall never go to sleep tonight,' said Belinda, and the others said the same. But when bedtime came they were all as sleepy as usual, of course.

Mummy came into their caravan to kiss them goodnight.

'I do like the new curtains,' said Belinda sleepily. 'Thank you, Mummy, for making them. They're all over buttercups and daisies and cornflowers and marigolds. It's like looking at a field.'

Ann kissed her mother goodnight too. 'Mummy,' she said, in her ear, 'the ship won't sail off with us on board, will it? It'll wait till we've gone, won't it?'

'Oh yes – don't you worry about that!' said Mummy. 'Go to sleep now, and the morning will come all the sooner. You're going to have a really lovely day!'

CHAPTER TWO
A Very Big Ship

Mike woke first the next morning, and he
remembered at once that it was Saturday –
and that they were all going to see the big
ship, *Queen Elizabeth*. He sat up and rubbed
his hands in joy.

'Wake up, girls! It's *Queen Elizabeth* day!'
he called, and Belinda and Ann woke with
a jump. They too remembered what was
going to happen, and they leapt out of their
comfortable little bunks like rabbits springing
from their holes.

Belinda flew down the steps of the caravan
to help with the breakfast. Mike ran to see if
there was plenty of wood for the fire. Ann

made the bunks very neatly and tidily. There wouldn't be much time for jobs after breakfast today!

They didn't even have time to wash up the breakfast things before Granny's car arrived at the field-gate! 'Honk! honk!' the horn sounded. 'Honk, honk!'

'There's the car!' cried Ann, in excitement, and nearly knocked the milk over. 'Mummy, Mummy, we aren't ready!'

'Well, we soon shall be – but not if you knock everything over,' said Mummy. 'Belinda, just pack all the things into the little sink so that we can wash them when we come back. Ann, Mike, go and get your hats and coats.'

Soon everyone was running over to the field-gate. Granny was in the car, looking out anxiously for them. Daddy opened the door and gave her a kiss.

'Hallo, hallo!' he said. 'Punctual as always. Good-morning, James. I hear you are going to be good enough to look after the caravans and the two horses for me today.'

The driver touched his cap. 'Yes, sir, I'd be delighted. Nice to have a day in a caravan in the country! And I'll see to the horses, sir. Davey and Clopper, aren't they?'

'Yes,' said the children. Ann touched his arm. 'You *will* go and talk to them, won't you?' she asked. 'They don't like it when we all go off for the day and nobody comes near them.'

'Don't you worry, miss – I'll ask them all their news,' said the driver, and he helped Mummy into the front seat.

Daddy got into the driving-seat. Ann sat on Mummy's knee in front. Mike and Belinda got in at the back, trying hard not to squash Granny too much. But she was a very little person and didn't really take up much more room than they did.

'Well, what a treat this is going to be!' said Granny. 'I was so surprised when Daddy rang me up last night. I've always wanted to see the

Queen Elizabeth – our most magnificent ship!'

This time they drove the whole way to Southampton. They stopped for lunch, sitting in the sun on a grassy hillside, looking down over a valley. Little fields separated by green hedges spread out before them.

'It's rather like a patchwork quilt,' said Belinda. 'All bits and pieces joined together by hedges. Is America like this, I wonder?'

'Oh no!' said Daddy. 'You wouldn't see any tiny fields like this, with hedges between. You'd see miles upon miles of great rolling fields, as far as the eye can reach. One field in America would take a hundred of our little fields – sometimes a thousand or more!'

'It must be a very, very big country then,' said Ann. 'I should get lost in it.'

'You probably would!' said Granny. 'But

as you're not going, you can feel quite safe here with me. Now – have we all finished our lunch? We ought to be setting off again.'

After a while they arrived at a big, familiar town. 'It's the port of Southampton,' Daddy declared, 'where big ships – and little ships too – come to harbour.'

'What a lot of cranes everywhere!' said Mike, watching a crane in the distance pulling up a great package. 'I suppose they're used to unload ships, aren't they?'

'Yes,' said Daddy. 'Do you see that little box-like house near the bottom of the crane? Well, a man sits in there all day long, and works the crane.'

'I'd rather like to do that,' said Mike. 'I once built a little crane with my Meccano, and it worked just like that big one.'

'Look! Aren't those the funnels of the *Queen Elizabeth*?' suddenly said Mummy, and she pointed beyond the crane. Daddy slowed down the car.

Two enormous red funnels showed above
the tops of the buildings beyond the crane.
'Yes,' said Daddy. 'That's the *Queen Elizabeth*.'

The children stared in awe. She was even
bigger than they remembered from their
holiday on the *Pole Star*. 'Are those her *funnels*?'
said Ann, hardly believing her eyes. 'Good
gracious – if her *funnels* are higher than
houses, what a *very* big ship she must be! Why,
you could almost drop a house down one of
her funnels!'

'Not quite,' said Mummy. The car went
on again through the crowded streets of
Southampton, and at last came to the docks.
What a wonderful place!

Mike couldn't take his eyes from the ships
there. Great big ships – smaller ships – quite
small ships. Fussy little tugs bustling here

and there. Boats everywhere. Hootings and sirens, and hammerings and shouts! What a wonderful place to live!

'I wish we lived at Southampton,' said Mike. 'I'd be down at the docks every day. I think I shall be a sailor when I grow up, Daddy.'

'Not an engine-driver after all?' said Daddy, stopping the car at a gate, and showing some tickets to the policeman there. 'Can we go through? Thank you.'

'The *Queen* is up beyond,' said the policeman, and saluted.

The car ran through the gateway, and Daddy put it in a parking-place where there were many other cars. Then they made their way to the *Queen Elizabeth*.

Ann didn't even know the *Elizabeth* when they came in sight of her. She hadn't expected anything so enormous. But the other two children gasped in surprise.

'Mummy! She's the biggest ship that was ever built!' cried Mike, as his eyes went up and up the sides of the great ship, past deck after deck, to the topmost one of all – then to the funnels that now towered far above him, higher than any house.

'She's grand,' said Daddy, proudly. 'I'm glad she's British. No one can beat us at ship-building. We've been ship-builders for centuries – and here's our grandest ship so far!'

'Let's go aboard – oh, do let's hurry up and go aboard!' cried Belinda. 'I want to see what she's like inside!'

CHAPTER THREE
Tea on the Queen Elizabeth

'Gangway for the *Queen Elizabeth*, sir? That one over there,' said a nearby sailor, and pointed to where a slanting gangway ran from the ship to the dock-side. Up they all went, and into the ship.

'We have to find Mr Harrison,' said Daddy, looking at his tickets. 'He will show us as much as he can.'

Mr Harrison was a very jolly man indeed. He wore officer's uniform, and greeted Daddy like an old friend.

'Good afternoon, sir. I was told you were coming. Now, how would you like to see over our little ship?'

Well, of course, it was anything but a little ship! The children were soon quite bewildered by all the different decks they were taken on – each deck seemed to stretch for miles! They went on the games deck too, and Mike wished they could have some games.

'Deck-tennis – ooh,' he said. 'And quoits – and shuffle-board. Oh Daddy, do people have time to play all these games on the way to America? There's such a lot of them.'

'Plenty of time,' said Daddy. 'Look – these are the lifeboats, slung up there ready for any emergency.'

'What's an emergency?' asked Ann.

'Oh – something like a terrible storm that might harm the ship and make it necessary for people to get off her in the lifeboats,' said Daddy. 'Or a fire aboard. You never know.

All big ships have lifeboats.'

'Daddy, I can't somehow think that we're on a ship,' said Belinda, as they walked down another big deck. 'It's so very big. Why, when I look over the deck-rail the ships down below look like toys!'

'And we can't feel any movement either, because the ship's too big to feel any waves in the dock,' said Mike. 'I'd like to feel what it's like when she rolls, though – or don't big ships like this roll?'

'My word, young man, you wouldn't like it if you were on board when the *Elizabeth* really *does* roll!' said the officer who was showing them round. 'Sometimes it seems as if she's never going to stop heeling over to one side – it feels as if she's going to go right down below the water before she rights herself a bit, and then rolls back and over to the other side! Ah, you want to be in a bit of a gale on this ship.'

'I wish I could be,' said Mike. 'I'd like that.'

'Well, what about tea?' asked the officer. 'It will be ready for you. I'll take you down to the dining-room in the lift.'

'In the *lift*?' echoed the children in astonishment. 'Is there really a lift on this ship?'

'Good gracious, yes – quite a lot,' said the officer, and led them into a big lounge between the fore and aft decks. At each side there were lifts. The doors of one slid open, and the children gazed into what looked like a little room.

'What a big lift!' said Ann. They all stepped in and down they went, past one, two, three floors – and then stopped.

'Fancy going down and down in a lift inside a ship!' said Mike. 'How many floors down does this lift go?'

'Fourteen,' said the officer. 'And after that there's yet another lift that goes down into the bowels of the ship.'

'Oooh – what an enormous dining-room!' said Belinda, as they went from the lift into a great, empty room.

'Yes – it holds hundreds and hundreds of people,' said the officer. 'You should see it when it's full of diners – and the band is playing – and great mounds of food are being carried about all over the place!'

But the dining-room was empty now and silent. The officer led them to a table in an alcove, set ready for tea. 'Here you are,' he said. 'Tea on the *Queen Elizabeth* for you! I hope you'll enjoy it!'

The children gazed in awe at the tea.

'What's that?' asked Ann, pointing to a plate of snow-white slices of what she thought must be cake.

'Bread and butter!' said Mummy. 'They have white bread aboard ship and in America. You'll like it.'

They did! They couldn't believe it was only bread and butter. It looked so beautifully white! And the cakes were amazing – all sugary and creamy and the prettiest shapes.

Belinda looked towards what were like two oblong cakes in the middle of the table.

'What are those?' she said. 'Can I have a slice, Granny?'

'Yes,' said Granny, and cut her a big one. It was in layers of three colours – pink, yellow and brown.

'Eat it with a spoon,' said Granny.

'Why?' asked Belinda in surprise. 'I don't eat a slice of cake with a spoon, do I?'

But she picked up her spoon and broke off a piece of the cake. Her eyes opened wide and she rolled them round at Mike and Ann in delight. She swallowed her mouthful.

'It's *ice-cream* cake!' she said. 'Would you believe it – we've got two great big cakes of ice-cream all to ourselves! Are we meant to eat them all, Mummy?'

'You won't be able to,' said her mother, laughing. 'Isn't it lovely? They have an enormous amount of ice-cream in America, you know – and these big ships must make tons of it for their passengers.'

'I wish we were passengers then,' said

Belinda. 'I *wish* we were going to America.
Do they have ice-cream every single day
like this? I wouldn't eat anything but that.
Mummy, have some!'

Everyone laughed at Belinda. She made up
her mind not to leave a single scrap of the ice-
cream cakes – but alas, they were so rich that
nobody could possibly manage more than one
slice. It was very sad.

They were sorry when they had to leave the big *Queen*. 'She's beautiful,' said Mike, as they went down the gangway and then stopped to look up at her great steep sides. 'How I wish I could live in her when she's really out on the sea!'

'Yes – she doesn't somehow seem like a real ship when she's here in dock,' said Mummy. 'But out at sea, when she's rolling and tossing – ah, that would be a wonderful thing!'

Mike and Belinda stood still to have one last look. 'I'm afraid it will be a long time before we see you again!' said Belinda, to the big ship. 'A very, very long time!'

But it wasn't. Surprising things were going to happen to Mike, Belinda and Ann!

CHAPTER FOUR
It Can't Be True!

The three children went back to school again the next week, full of their visit to the *Queen Elizabeth*. The boys and girls listened, and wished they had gone too, especially when they heard about the marvellous lifts and the wonderful ice-cream cake.

Then, when Mike, Belinda and Ann went home the next Friday, what a surprise they had! Daddy was home before them, his face one big smile. Mummy was smiling too, and looked very excited indeed!

'Why is Daddy home so early?' asked Mike. 'And why do you look so excited, Mummy?'

'We were waiting to ask you something,'

said Mummy. 'It's this – how would you all like to sail away on the *Queen Elizabeth*, and spend two weeks in New York?'

There wasn't a sound from the three children. They stared as if they couldn't have heard right. Mike opened and shut his mouth like a goldfish.

'Tongue-tied!' said Daddy, with a laugh. 'Say something, one of you, or you'll most certainly burst!'

Then all three yelled at the same time.

'Do you really mean it?'

'Is it really true?'

'When do we GO?'

Ann flung herself on her father. 'Tell us about it, Daddy. It isn't a joke, is it?'

'No,' said Daddy. 'It's quite true. The man who was going is ill – and so the firm have

asked me to go instead. I'm allowed to take
Mummy – and Granny says she will pay part
of your fares if I like to take you as well for
the trip.'

'She says it would do you a lot of good to see America – it will be like living in a geography lesson,' said Mummy. 'What do you think of that?'

'Mummy! I can't believe it,' said Mike. 'When do we go? And what about school?'

'You'll have to miss school for two or three weeks, I'm afraid,' said Mummy. 'But it will really be a great experience for you – a real education! Fancy Granny saying you ought to go – and helping to pay for you!'

'Good old Granny,' said Belinda. 'She's the kindest person in the world – except you and Daddy!'

'You still haven't said when we *go*,' said Mike.

'We go when the *Elizabeth* comes back,' said Mummy. 'She will be back here again next week. She's at New York now – and she leaves there tonight or tomorrow morning. We shall sail next Friday, or very early the next morning rather.'

'Next Friday!' said Belinda, her eyes shining. 'Next *Friday*! We'll have to come back home to the caravans then.'

'Yes – you must come home on Wednesday,' said Mummy. 'Then I can get your clothes and things ready, and pack. We have to be on board Friday night.'

'Shall we have to go to bed on board while she's in Southampton?' asked Mike. 'I would have liked to see her slipping out of the port by daylight. Shan't we see her leaving England?'

'Don't look so solemn!' said Mummy. 'The *Queen* has to be guided by the tide. You'll be fast asleep when she leaves – and you'll wake up to find her far out at sea in the morning!'

'And we shan't see land again for days!' said Belinda.

'Oh yes, you will,' said her mother. 'The *Elizabeth* goes to Cherbourg in France before she goes to America – so you'll see land the very next day.'

'Oh – shall we see France too, then?' asked Ann, in delight. 'Can we go ashore?'

'Dear me, no,' said Daddy. 'We shall probably stay outside Cherbourg, and watch the little steamers chugging out from the port with new passengers for the *Elizabeth*. You can watch that. You'll like it.'

'I can't believe it's true,' sighed Belinda. 'I thought last Saturday was wonderful enough – having tea on board – but *next* Saturday

we'll be sailing over the ocean in the biggest
ship in the world.'

'Can I take my doll Josephine?' asked Ann.

'It would be an education for her too.'

Daddy laughed. 'Yes – you take her – she

shall meet the American dolls and see how she likes them. Some of them don't only go to sleep, and talk, but they can walk too. We'll see what Josephine says to that.'

The children could hardly do any lessons at all the next week. They kept thinking of the *Queen Elizabeth*, and seeing her great red funnels towering high above her spotless decks.

'I know I shall get lost on such a big ship,' said Ann to Belinda. 'It's as big as a small town! I'll never know my way about.'

'We'll soon get used to it,' said Belinda. 'Did you know there was a swimming-pool, Ann? We couldn't see it when we went, because it was shut up – but there is one. We can go swimming in it.'

'Don't tell me any more,' begged Ann. 'It's beginning to sound like a fairy-tale – and I do want it to be true.'

It was true, of course. Wednesday came, and the children caught the bus to go home to the caravans.

'We've come!' cried Ann, seeing her mother waiting at the gate. 'It's Wednesday at last.'

'And soon it will be Friday,' said Mike. 'Only one more day – then Friday!'

Thursday was a busy day of washing clothes and packing lots of things. Ann wouldn't let her doll be packed. 'No – she wants to *see* everything,' she said. 'I'll carry her, Mummy.'

Thursday night came – the last to be spent in the caravans for some time. Then Friday morning dawned, fair and bright – a really lovely October day.

'It's Friday, it's Friday!' sang the three

children as soon as they woke up. It didn't take them long to get dressed *that* day!

'We must say goodbye to Davey and Clopper,' said Ann. So they went to find the two horses and hugged them.

'We're going to America,' said Ann. 'But we'll come back. Goodbye, Davey, goodbye, Clopper. Be good, and I *might* perhaps send you a postcard!'

CHAPTER FIVE
On Board at Last!

Granny lent them her car again, to drive down to Southampton. She didn't come with them because there wasn't room for her and all the luggage too. As it was, the children had to sit with suitcases all round their feet!

'Have you got our tickets, Daddy?' asked Ann, anxiously. 'Shall we get there in time? Suppose we have a puncture? Will the boat wait for us?'

'We'll be all right,' said Daddy. 'Yes, I've got the tickets, and I know which cabins we've got and everything.'

It didn't really seem very long before they were in Southampton again. Daddy took them to a little hotel to have supper. It was all very exciting.

They could hardly eat anything. Mike was anxious to go. 'We might be too late to get on,' he said. 'We really ought to go.'

'Mike – the boat doesn't sail till about half-past one at *night*,' said Daddy. 'Or rather, in the very early morning, long before dawn, while it's still pitch-dark.'

'Oh,' said Mike, and decided to eat something after all.

'Shall we be seasick?' said Ann, suddenly.

'Not a bit,' said Mummy, at once. 'And if you are, it soon passes. Now do eat that pudding, Ann.'

At last they were at the dock again, and at last they were walking up the gangway. But this time there seemed to be hundreds and hundreds of people walking on too! The children stared at them in wonder.

'Are they all going to America?' said Mike.

'Most of them,' said Daddy. 'Some are just going to see their friends off, of course. The ship looks different now, doesn't she, since the Saturday we saw her with hardly anyone on board?'

She did look different. It was night now
and there were lights everywhere. The round
portholes glittered like hundreds of eyes, and
there was such a noise that Mike had to shout
to hear himself speak.

'Keep close to me,' said Daddy. 'Our cabins
are together, so we shall be all right once
we've found them.'

They did find them at last. Belinda looked
at them in awe. They were quite big, and
had beds, not bunks. The big round porthole
looked out over the dock, and she saw
thousands of twinkling lights out there. She
imagined what it would be like when she
looked out in a day or two's time and saw
nothing but sea.

'There's every single thing you want,' said
Mike, looking round his mother's cabin.
'Wash-basin – dressing-table – wardrobe –
drawers – and look, when you put this flap
down, Mummy, it makes a little desk for you
to write on!'

The three children had a cabin with three
beds in. They were delighted. 'Can I have the
one by the port-hole?' begged Belinda. 'Oh
Mike, do let me. I want to be able to stand

on the bed and look out of the port-hole any time in the night that I wake up.'

'Well, you won't see anything if you do,' said Mike. He looked longingly at the bed by the porthole. He badly wanted it himself, but he was very unselfish with his two sisters.

'All right,' he said, with a sigh. 'You can

have the bed by the porthole going to America, Belinda, and Ann can have it coming back.'

'I don't want a bed by the porthole,' said Ann. 'I don't like to be as near the sea as that. I'm afraid it might leak in on me.'

'You're silly,' said Mike, cheering up. 'Well, if that's what you're afraid of, you can have the inside bed each time. I'll have the porthole bed coming back from America.'

A nice bright face with twinkling eyes popped round the door. 'Ah – I've got three children in this cabin of mine this time, have I? That's nice.'

The children stared at her. She looked very nice and crisp and clean – rather like a nurse, the children thought. She laughed at their faces.

'I'm your stewardess,' she said. 'I look after you. If ever you want me, just ring that bell over there – and I'll come trotting along to see which of you is sick, or wants a hot-water bottle, or some more to eat!'

The children laughed. They liked this stewardess. 'Would you like something to eat now?' she said. 'I expect you've had your supper, haven't you? But would you like some nice sugary biscuits, and a big glass of creamy milk each – or some orange juice?'

All this sounded very nice. 'I'd love the biscuits and some orange juice,' said Belinda and the others said the same. Then Mummy came in, and smiled to hear that they had ordered eats and drinks already!

She began to unpack a few things for them. She laid their night things on the beds and set out their tooth-brushes and washing things.

'You behave exactly as if you were at home,' she said. 'Cleaning your teeth, washing, brushing your hair and everything.'

'And saying our prayers,' said Ann. 'I'm going to ask God to keep us safe when we're on the deep sea. I'd like him to keep a special lifeboat for me if anything happens.'

'You've got a special lifeboat already,' said Mummy. 'I'll show you yours tomorrow. And in that cupboard you've each got a special cork life jacket. You will have to learn how to put it on tomorrow.'

Belinda sighed. 'Everything is so lovely and exciting,' she said. 'Fancy having cork jackets of our own, too. I shall love to put mine on.'

'Now you must go to bed,' said Mummy. 'It's long past your bedtime. And here comes your nice stewardess with biscuits and orange-juice – and what biscuits!'

They certainly were wonderful ones. The three children hurriedly undressed, cleaned their teeth, washed, and brushed their hair, and hopped into bed.

'I shall say my prayers last of all,' said Ann. 'Then I can say thank you for these biscuits too. Oh dear – I'm sure I shall never go to sleep tonight!'

'I'm going to keep awake,' said Mike. 'I want to hear the anchor come up – and hear the fussy little tugs pulling away at the big *Queen* to get her out to sea. I want to feel her moving as she leaves Southampton.'

'Oh, so do I!' cried Belinda. But she and Ann fell fast asleep. Only Mike lay awake, waiting.

CHAPTER SIX
Goodbye to England

More and more passengers came on board
the big ship, and found their different cabins.
Cranes worked busily and loaded the
enormous holds with luggage. There was a
great deal of noise and bustle and excitement.

Belinda and Ann slept through it all. They
were tired out with excitement. Mike kept
awake for two hours, and then he felt his
eyelids closing because they were so heavy. He
propped them up with his fingers.

But then his fingers felt heavy, and slid
down from his eyes. His eyes closed. He
slept too. Poor Mike – he had so much
wanted to be awake when the time came

for the *Elizabeth* to leave the big port of
Southampton.

Half-past one came. The tide was right.
Little tugs fussed up in the darkness, and ropes
were thrown from the big ship over to them.
How was it possible for such tiny tugs to move
such an enormous ship?

But they did. Gradually the *Queen Elizabeth*
moved away from the dock-side. Gradually
she left Southampton docks behind.

Mike awoke with a jump. He felt a
peculiar movement far below him. He sat up,
wondering what it was. Then he knew! The
Queen Elizabeth was moving!

'She's away!' he thought and got out
of bed. He groped his way to Belinda's bed,
which was by the big porthole. He wondered
if he would wake her if he stood up on her

bed and looked out.

He cautiously got up on the bed. Belinda woke at once. 'Who is it?' she said, in a frightened voice. 'Where am I?'

'Sh! It's me, Mike! Belinda – the *Elizabeth* is moving! I felt her just now. Can *you* feel her? She's not keeping still any more. You can feel the water running under her!'

Belinda was thrilled. She knelt up to the porthole and the two of them looked out. They whispered together.

'Yes – we've left the dock-side. We must be right in the middle of the harbour. Look at all the lights slipping past.'

'Doesn't the water look a long long way down?' said Mike. 'And so awfully black! And look at all the lights twinkling in it, reflected from the dock-side.'

'Now she's left the dock,' said Belinda. 'Is she going backwards, Mike? She must be, to get out of the dock. Soon we shall feel her stopping – and then going the other way, shan't we?'

Belinda was quite right. The *Elizabeth* stopped when she was well out of the dock, and then began to move the other way.

The little tugs hooted in farewell and chugged off by themselves. They had done their job.

'There goes a little tug,' said Mike, seeing one dimly in the starlit darkness. 'Aren't they clever, Belinda, the way they push and pull, and get a big ship like this safely out of the docks? I wouldn't mind having a tug of my own.'

'Now we're really going,' said Belinda, softly. 'I suppose we'll keep along the coast a bit – but by the time morning comes we'll be out of sight of land.'

'Till we reach France,' said Mike. 'And then we'll be days on the enormous Atlantic Ocean, hundreds of miles from anywhere.'

They were silent. The *Elizabeth* was big – but the ocean was vast. Belinda shivered a little. Then she thought of the big lifeboats and the life jacket and felt more cheerful. She watched the line of far-off lights that gradually passed behind them as the big ship ploughed on through the dark waters.

'I like to feel we're really moving, don't you, Mike?' said Belinda. 'I like the little rolls the ship gives now and again when a bigger wave than usual passes under her. Isn't this *fun*?'

The cabin door opened cautiously, and light streamed in from the passage outside. The two children looked round. They saw Mummy outlined in the doorway.

'Mummy!' said Belinda, in a loud whisper. 'Mummy, we've left Southampton now – did you know? We're off to America!'

'Sh!' said Mummy. 'You'll wake Ann. I wondered if you two were awake. Yes, we're really on our way now. I hope you didn't keep awake all the time.'

'No,' said Belinda. 'I only woke about twenty minutes ago.'

'Well, cuddle down into bed again now,' said Mummy. 'I won't stay in case I wake Ann. Mike, get back to your bed, dear.'

'Right,' said Mike and slipped down from Belinda's bed. 'Mummy, will you come and fetch us in the morning? We wouldn't know how to find the dining-room.'

'Of course I'll come,' said Mummy. 'Now, good-night, dears. Go to sleep at once.'

The door shut. Mike yawned. He really felt very sleepy indeed. He called softly to Belinda. 'Good-night, Belinda!'

But there was no answer. Belinda had curled up and was already fast asleep!

They all slept very soundly indeed in their

comfortable little beds. They were awakened by a loud knocking on the door. Belinda woke in a fright, and sat up. She felt sure the boat must be sinking or something!

Then the stewardess put her head round the door, smiling. 'Sleepyheads, aren't you? This is the third time I've been along. Your mother says, will you get up now, because she will be ready to take you down to breakfast in ten minutes' time.'

'Oooh yes,' said Mike, scrambling out of bed. 'What's for breakfast, stewardess? Do you know?'

'Porridge, cereals, iced melon, stewed fruit, bacon, eggs, steak, fish, omelettes, chops, ham, tongue . . .' she began.

The children stared at her in amazement. 'Do we *have* to eat all that?' asked Mike.

The stewardess laughed. 'You can choose
whatever you want, eat as much as you like,
and take as long over it as you wish!' she said.
'So hurry up now, and get down to a really
fine breakfast!'

They certainly did hurry up – and when
Mummy came for them, they were all ready.

Down in the lift they went to the enormous dining-room – and found their table. And when the menu came, the children simply didn't know what to choose from the dozens and dozens of things on it!

'If all the meals are like this, I *am* going to enjoy this trip!' said Mike.

CHAPTER SEVEN
A Wonderful Ship

That first day on the *Queen Elizabeth* was simply marvellous to the three children. At first they wouldn't go anywhere without their mother or father, because they really were afraid of getting lost!

'Everything's so *big*,' said Belinda. 'The decks are miles and miles long. It takes ages to go all round the ship on just one deck!'

They went to see the big swimming-pool, and Mummy said they might bathe there some time. They went to see the beautiful library with hundreds and hundreds of books waiting to be read. They found the children's corner there, and each of them borrowed a book to read.

'Though goodness knows when we'll have time to read a book on this lovely ship!' said Mike.

There were shops on the *Queen Elizabeth* too! The children went to look at them – all kinds of shops that sold anything the passengers wanted. How odd to have shops on a ship!

It was great fun up on the sports deck. It was windy up there, and the children had to hold on to their hats. They went to watch the grown-ups playing games.

There were games with rope rings. There were games with great wooden discs that had to be pushed very hard indeed with a big wooden pusher. That was called shuffle-board. The children waited till the grown-ups had finished playing with the shuffle-board, and then they had a try.

But they couldn't push the great wooden counters very far! They tried their hand at throwing the rope rings on to numbered squares, and Mike was so good at that, that Daddy had a game with him. Mike nearly won!

'It's nice up here on the sports deck,' said Belinda, her cheeks glowing with the strong breeze. 'It isn't all enclosed with glass windows like the other decks down below – you can really taste the spray up here, and feel the wind. I like it.'

The great sea spread out round them for miles. Always there was the plash-plash-plash of waves against the ship's sides – a lovely sound. She left behind her a long white trail of foaming water.

'That's called the wake,' said Daddy. So they watched the wake forming behind the ship, spreading away as far as they could see.

'The fishes must be very astonished when a big ship like this comes by,' said Belinda, looking down into the water.

'I should be frightened if *I* were a fish and

I suddenly saw a great thing like this coming towards me,' said Ann. 'I should swim away quickly.'

'We're going fast now, aren't we, Daddy?' said Mike.

Daddy nodded. 'Yes – she's a fast ship, the *Elizabeth*. So is her sister, the *Queen Mary*.'

At eleven o'clock they went downstairs and found their own deck-chairs on the deck below. Mummy said that it was about time that deck stewards brought round little cups of hot soup and biscuits for everyone.

'Good gracious!' said Belinda. 'Do we really have hot soup in the middle of the morning? I do think this is a ship with good ideas!'

Sure enough the stewards appeared with trays of hot steaming soup in little bowls. There were biscuits to go with it. It was

simply delicious. The children wondered if they might have another helping each, but Mummy said no.

'You will want to have an enormous lunch at one o'clock,' she said. 'Don't spoil it! It will take you about ten minutes to read all down the menu!'

After that they went to see the gym, where people were doing all kinds of exercises. There was a peculiar-looking imitation horse there, and Mike got on it. Up came the instructor, pulled a handle – and dear me,

that horse came alive and began to do such extraordinary things that Mike nearly fell off! He clutched it hard round the neck and tried to stop himself slipping. Belinda and Ann screamed with laughter.

The horse bucked and reared and rocked from side to side till Mike yelled for mercy. He was very glad when it stopped and he was able to get off. Belinda got on and had a turn, but Ann wouldn't. She was quite certain she would fall off at once.

'This is a wonderful ship,' said Mike, happily. 'There's simply *everything* here – it's like a small town all neatly put together with everything anyone can want.'

They went up on the sports deck again after a lunch that was good enough to eat in a king's palace. 'Even the menu is like a book!'

said Belinda, marvelling at the wonderful coloured cover. 'And look at the inside! Mummy, can we *really* choose any of these dishes? I simply don't know what to have.'

'I'm beginning with iced melon – then chicken soup – and two little chops with tomatoes and onions and mushrooms – and an ice-cream called Bombe-something,' said Ann, unexpectedly. 'And I think I'll finish up with iced melon too!'

It really took quite a long time deciding what they were going to have, but nobody seemed in a hurry at all. 'After all, no one's got a train or a bus to catch,' said Mike. 'There's all day long to choose food and games and wander round.'

They all felt rather full after such a marvellous meal, and went up on the sports deck in the wind. It was nice up there. The sun shone, the sky was blue, and the sea was very blue too. Ann sat down in a corner and fell fast asleep!

She was awakened by a most terrible noise. She leapt up in a fright, yelling for her mother. 'Mummy, Mummy, what is it? Are we sinking? Have we hit a rock?'

But it was only the siren of the *Queen Elizabeth* hooting loudly because she was coming near France. It was such a sudden and tremendous noise that everyone looked startled for a moment.

'There's France!' Mike told Ann. 'Daddy says that port is Cherbourg. We're not going right into the harbour because it's a bit rough here. So they're sending out boats to us with new passengers, and taking off passengers that want to go to France.'

Out came two little steamers from Cherbourg, and the *Queen Elizabeth* stayed quite still, waiting.

'Isn't it fun?' said Mike, leaning over the sports-deck rail to watch. 'How small those steamers look! I'm glad I belong to the *Queen Elizabeth*. It makes me feel very important!'

CHAPTER EIGHT
Out on the Ocean

That first day seemed deliciously long
and full of excitement and surprises. They
were all very tired when they went to bed.
The *Elizabeth* had left the coast of France,
and was now on her way to America! The
sea wasn't quite so smooth and calm, and
sometimes the children staggered a little as
they walked down the passage to their cabin.

'One day gone,' said Mike. 'I hope the
days don't go *too* quickly! I wonder what
we do tomorrow. It will be Sunday. How can
we go to church? I haven't seen a church here,
have you?'

'You couldn't build a church on a ship,' said

Ann. 'We'll have to see what happens.'

Mummy told them the next morning that there were two things that day that she wanted them to do.

'There is a church service at eleven o'clock,' she said, 'and you must put on your hats and coats just as if you were going to a real church, although the service is only being held in the big lounge. You must each take pennies for a collection too.'

'Fancy going to church on a ship!' said Ann. 'I do like that. What's the second thing we have to go to, Mummy?'

'Lifeboat drill,' said Mummy. 'We all have to get out our life jackets from the cupboards in our cabins and put them on properly. Then we have to go up to our boat stations . . .'

'Boat stations! Are there stations here, then?'

asked Mike. 'I haven't seen them!'

'They're not really *stations*,' said Mummy. 'Just places where we meet for lifeboat drill – or to get our lifeboat if there was any need to.'

'How do we know which is our boat-station?' asked Belinda.

Mummy showed her some directions on a card in the cabin. 'This shows you the way to yours,' she said. 'Up the stairs, and up again. On to that deck. And go to the place on the deck marked with your number. It's quite easy. There are many different stations, and each passenger must know his own.'

'So that if the boat was wrecked, we'd all know where to go at once, and be helped into our life-boats, I suppose,' said Mike. 'That's very sensible.'

They went to church service at eleven

o'clock, looking very proper in hats and coats. Ann even put her gloves on.

It was very like a real church service except that there were no proper pews, only chairs, and it seemed extraordinary to look out of the windows and see miles of green–blue sea outside instead of houses and streets.

Ann was very pleased with one hymn that ended each verse with:

Oh, hear us when we cry to Thee

For those in peril on the sea.

'That's a very good hymn to sing on a ship,' she said afterwards. 'I'm glad there's a hymn that prays for people on the sea.'

The captain gave a short, interesting little sermon, and everyone listened. There were

more hymns and prayers and a collection.
Belinda thought it was the nicest church
service she had ever been to in her life. It was
peculiar to feel the ship moving all the time,
and to see the white clouds racing by as the
ship moved along.

'Now for lifeboat drill,' said Mummy, and
took them to their cabin to get their life jackets.
A loud bell rang out and made them jump.

'That's to warn everyone to go to their
lifeboat stations,' said Mummy. 'If ever we hear
that in the middle of the night, up we must
get, snatch at our life jackets and run to our
stations as fast as ever we can.'

This sounded very exciting, but none of the
children wanted it to happen!

They got their life jackets and Mummy
showed them how to tie them round them.

They began to laugh.

'We look *enormous*!' said Mike. 'Do look at Ann. She's as broad as she's long!'

'Hurry up,' said Mummy. 'This is a thing we always have to be quick about, even if it's only practice.'

Soon they all had their life jackets on, and Mummy and Daddy took them to the deck where their boat-station was. About fifty people were with them. Farther along there were other groups of people. Every passenger had his own boat-station, and now he knew where to go for it.

'And, you see, in a real emergency, when the life-boats are lowered for us to get into,' said Daddy, 'everyone gets into his own lifeboat, and there are just the right number. Then down the boat goes into the sea, and is cast off to safety.'

'All the same, I hope it won't happen,' said Ann, looking rather scared.

'No, it won't,' said Mummy. 'But it's good to know what we must do if it *should* happen.'

When everyone was at his boat-station, an officer came up to Daddy's group. He went round to see that everyone's life jacket was on properly. Then he talked to them all, and told them exactly what to do if the ship met with an accident.

The children were glad to go back to their cabins and take off their bulky life jackets. 'Is it dinner-time yet?' asked Ann. 'I had an enormous breakfast, and soup and biscuits at half-past ten, and now I feel hungry all over again.'

'I suppose you'll start off with iced melon

again?' said Mike, with a grin. 'So far, you've begun every single meal with iced melon. You'll turn into a melon yourself if you go on like this.'

'And do you know what *you'll* turn into?' said Ann, as they went to get into the lift to go down to the big dining-room. 'You'll turn into a chocolate ice-cream – and you'll be lucky if I don't eat you!'

CHAPTER NINE
A Gale Blows Up

The days began to slip away, but on the fourth day things suddenly changed. Great clouds came over the sea, and huge waves began to form in the strong wind that blew.

Then the *Queen Elizabeth* showed that, big or not, she was a ship that took notice of big waves! She began to roll from side to side. First this side a little, then back to the other side.

The children began to stagger a little as they went about the ship, which they now knew very well indeed. 'I hope she doesn't roll any farther over,' said Mike. 'I'm not sure I like it very much.'

'Why? Do you feel sick?' asked Ann.

'No. But I just don't *want* her to roll any farther over,' said Mike. However, she took no notice of Mike's wishes, and began to roll more than ever.

When night came ropes had been put up on the decks so that people might hold on to them as they went. The children were quite glad when bedtime came. At least their beds felt firm and safe!

But it was most peculiar to lie on a bed that slanted sideways when the ship rolled! 'I feel as if I ought to hold on to the sides in case I fall out,' said Ann.

When the light was out, it seemed as if the ship's rolling felt worse than ever. Down – down – down – to one side, until the children really thought they must be touching the water – then up, up, up, and over to the other side – down – down – down again, lower and lower till Ann sat up.

'I don't like it,' she wailed. 'Suppose it rolled so far over that it didn't come back!'

The stewardess put her head round the door. 'Who's this shouting out?' she said, and switched on the light. 'Dear me, surely you're not making a fuss about a bit of a gale like

this? You want to be in a *real* storm to have
something worth shouting about!'

'Isn't this a real storm, then?' asked Ann.

'Good gracious no. It'll be gone by the
morning,' said the stewardess. 'A big ship
always rolls a bit in a gale – she can't help
it. But you want to be out in a small boat to
know what pitching and tossing and rolling
are really like!'

All the children were relieved to feel that
there wasn't much likelihood of the alarm
bell's sounding for them to put on life jackets,
rush to their boat-stations and get into a
lifeboat!

'Now you just listen to what I say,' said
the stewardess. 'The gale's beginning to die
down even now – we're only touching the
fringe of the storm and we'll soon be out of it.

You must enjoy the rolling instead of getting scared of it! You want a ship to behave like a ship, don't you?'

She said goodnight and went. 'Well, we shall certainly have something to tell the children at school about when we get back home,' said Mike, sleepily. 'I'm going to pretend I'm in a rocking-bed and enjoy it!'

'So am I,' said Belinda. 'That's a good idea.'

Ann didn't say anything. She had suddenly remembered something. What did a storm matter? What did a rolling ship matter? Hadn't she prayed to God that very night to keep them all safe – and here she was thinking He couldn't manage to protect them in even a *little* gale!

'That's very bad of me, and very untrusting,' she thought. 'I'm not afraid any more now.'

And she fell asleep thinking of the hymn they had sung on Sunday, which now seemed an even more sensible hymn than ever,

Oh, hear us when we cry to Thee

For those in peril on the sea.

The stewardess was right. The *Elizabeth* sailed right out of the gale by the morning, and when the children woke up, what a difference! The big ship hardly rolled at all – all the guide-ropes had been taken down – and people who had felt seasick came down to make a good breakfast.

And now the great excitement was the arrival at New York! The gale had slowed down the *Elizabeth*, and instead of arriving that night she would not arrive till ten o'clock the next morning.

'Which will be very nice,' said Daddy, 'because you will be able to watch the coastline all the way up the big river to New York. And we shall pass something that the Americans are very proud of – the colossal Statue of Liberty, holding a great torch aloft.'

'All the same – I feel quite sad now to think we're going to leave the *Queen Elizabeth*,' said Belinda, looking solemn. 'I've got used to her, and I love her.'

'Well, we're going *back* in her, in two or three weeks' time, aren't we?' said Mike. 'You'll have another trip just like this.'

'Except that the clocks will have to be put forward each day, instead of back,' said Mummy. That had been a very funny thing to happen, the children thought.

Every day their clocks had been set back an hour, because they were travelling westwards, so they had gained an hour in their day. But when they returned eastwards they would lose an hour each day – the clocks would be set an hour forward!

It seemed funny to meddle about with time like that – but, as they already knew, the time in New York wasn't the same as the time in England at that particular moment!

They were all excited to see land again. They passed into the great river and watched the enormous buildings on each side. 'Much, much bigger than ours,' said Mike.

'You wait till you see some of the high buildings in New York!' said Daddy. 'You won't believe your eyes!'

'There's the Statue of Liberty!' said somebody,

suddenly, and everyone craned their necks
to see the enormous and magnificent statue,
guarding the entrance to New York harbour.
Only the stewards did not bother to look –
they had seen New York before.

'America at last!' said Mike, excited.
'The newest country in the world – and one
of the finest! When do we land, Daddy? I can
hardly wait!'

But he had to wait, of course, and at last their turn came to walk down the gangway and on to American soil.

'America!' said Ann, holding up her doll Josephine. 'Take a look, Josephine – you've come halfway across the world – and now we're in America!'

CHAPTER TEN
America at Last

New York was a most extraordinary city to Mike, Belinda and Ann. They stepped off the *Elizabeth* and marvelled to see how the big ship stretched herself right over the street. Her huge bows rose above some of the buildings, and this looked very peculiar.

They took a large yellow taxi to their hotel. The taxi-driver spoke exactly like they had heard many people speak on the films.

'He said "twenny-foor" instead of "twenty-four",' whispered Ann to Mike. 'Like Mickey Mouse talks on the films. Is that the American language?'

The taxi drove very fast indeed, and

whenever they came to red traffic lights it pulled up with a terrific jerk. Then all the taxis waiting began to hoot loudly without stopping.

'Oh dear,' said Mummy. 'Does this go on all the time?'

'You'll soon get so used to the noise of New York streets that you just won't notice it after a day or two,' said Daddy. 'Look, children – do you see those skyscrapers over there?'

They looked – and gasped. The buildings were so tall that they had to crane back their necks to see the tops of them as they raced past. Floor after floor after floor – however many storeys were there?

'You wanna see the Empire State Building,' said the taxi-driver, joining suddenly in the conversation. 'That's what you wanna see.

Over a hundred floors. Yes, *sir*!'

'*Can* we, Daddy?' asked Mike, eagerly. 'Do we go up in a lift? Can we go to the very top?'

'You've got to take more than one lift if you wanna get to the top of the Empire State building,' said the taxi-driver. 'You go right to the top and have a looksee round. You'll see little old New York all right then, and a lot more too!'

Some of the streets were very dark because the walls of the very tall buildings rose opposite one another and kept out the sun. Lights burned in many of the windows in those streets, though it was full daylight.

'Why don't *we* build skyscrapers in London?' asked Belinda. 'It certainly does save a lot of space.'

'New York is built on hard rock,' said Daddy. 'It will bear tremendous weights. We couldn't build enormous buildings like this in London – they would gradually sink with their weight!'

'It's a very good name – skyscrapers,' said Ann. 'They do really look as if they must be scraping the sky, Daddy.'

'New York's not a *bit* like London,' said Mike. 'The streets are so wide and straight – and quite straight streets run off the main avenue. There aren't any winding streets, or higgledy-piggledy ones, as there are in London.'

'Ah, London grew, but New York was planned,' said Daddy. 'They are both beautiful in their own way. Now look, this is Broadway. At night the lights here – the advertisement signs – are wonderful. I'll bring you out to see them.'

They came to their hotel at last. It was a skyscraper too, though not a very big one. Mike looked at the number of floors marked on the lift – thirty-two! Goodness, no wonder the lift shot up at such a speed. It would take all day to go from the bottom to the top if it didn't go so quickly!

They unpacked their things and settled in. They thought their bedrooms were enormous after the ones on the *Elizabeth*. They looked out of the window and gave a gasp.

They were so high up that the people down in the road looked like ants! The children stared in amazement.

'Look at those cars!' said Mike. 'Honestly, they don't look as big as my dinky-cars at home!'

'No, they don't,' said Belinda. 'They just don't look real. They're so small they make me feel as if I must suddenly have become a giant – so that everyone looks tiny to me!'

'I don't like the feeling very much,' said Ann. 'Nor does Josephine. I shan't look out any more.'

Meals in America were enormous. The menus seemed even longer than those on the *Elizabeth*. The children gazed at them in astonishment, when they went down to a meal in the restaurant.

'Waffles! What are they?' asked Ann. 'They sound like the name for a rabbit or something. Hamburgers – Mummy, are they nice? And oh, look – hot-dogs! Can I have a hot-dog? Not if it's *really* dog, though. I wouldn't want to eat a dog.'

Everyone laughed. Ann looked round and her eyes opened wide when she saw the enormous platefuls of food that the waiters were setting in front of the guests.

'Have we got to eat so much?' she said to her mother. 'We had big helpings on the *Queen Elizabeth*, but these are even bigger.'

'I'll ask for small helpings for you,' said Mummy. So she did. But dear me, they were still so big that the children could do no more than nibble at them!

'Oh Mummy – will it all be wasted?' said
Belinda, who knew how careful her mother
was with food at home. 'What will happen to
it?'

'It'll go into the pig-bucket, I expect,' said
Mummy. 'The Americans waste far more than
we eat – but it's America, and that's the way
they like to live. I daresay if we had as much
food as they had, we'd be the same!'

'Oh dear – I don't like to leave so much,'
groaned Belinda, 'but I shall be ill if I eat
all this.'

'English people don't eat much,' said the
waiter, taking her plate and smiling.

'Let's go out on Broadway now,' said Mike,
looking out of the windows. 'It's dark. We
could see the lights, Daddy. I'd like to do that.'

So out they went on Broadway to see one
of the sights of the world – the masses of
twinkling, racing, jigging, blazing, brilliant
lights on all the tall buildings everywhere.
What a sight it was.

'Better than fireworks on Bonfire Night!'
said Ann. And it really was!

CHAPTER ELEVEN
A Wonderful City

The Americans were very friendly. As soon as Daddy met the people he had come over to see, they asked to meet his little family.

They made a great fuss of the children, and said they had wonderful manners. Mummy thought secretly that they had much better manners than the American children, who spoke loudly and were often rude to grown-ups. She felt proud of her three.

Nobody could have been nicer or more generous than their friends in New York. Every day Mummy found fresh flowers in her room sent by one friend or another. If she was asked out to dinner a beautiful box would arrive, tied up with magnificent ribbon – and inside would be a lovely buttonhole or shoulder-spray of flowers.

The children were not forgotten either. 'Look,' squealed Ann, coming into her mother's room with a parcel she had undone. 'Did you EVER see such a box of sweets in your life! Mummy, LOOK!'

Mummy looked. So did the others. It was certainly magnificent. The box was covered with bits of ribbon made to look like flowers, and had a big sash of ribbon round it – far better than any hair-ribbon Ann had!

Inside were layers upon layers of wonderful sweets. 'Candies, the Americans call them,' said Mike. 'Oh, Ann – what a *magical* box. They look too good to be eaten.'

'Have one?' said Ann, and soon they were

all eating the candies, which were certainly nicer than any they had ever had in their lives.

Belinda had a doll sent to her, and Mike had a wonderful pistol. It could shoot water, but if you fitted a bulb to the tip, it would light up like a torch when you pulled the trigger – and if you took out the bulb and put in a little paper of cartridges it would go off pop-pop-pop at top speed when the trigger was pulled.

Belinda's doll could walk. Belinda could hardly believe it when she saw it walk rather unsteadily over the floor, one foot after the other.

'Oh!' she cried, 'just look. She's far, far better than Josephine, Ann.'

'She's not,' said Ann, hugging Josephine.

'Anyway, I don't want Josephine to walk. Her legs aren't strong enough yet.'

Flowers, candies, fruit, chocolate, toys, books – everyone showered presents on the little English family. Surely there couldn't be more friendly or generous people in the world? Invitations poured down on them too – dinner-parties, afternoon parties, all kinds of parties. Mummy had to buy the children new clothes, because they really hadn't brought enough with them!

'I don't know *how* we're going to return all this friendliness,' said Daddy, in despair. 'The Americans are rich, and English people are poor – I haven't enough money to repay all this kindness.'

But the Americans didn't want any return. It was just their way. They liked Daddy and his family, and they wanted to show it.

The children lived in a whirl. There was hardly time to go sight-seeing at first. Mummy took them to see the shops, which were full of the most beautiful things in the world. She took them to a cake-shop too, and the children blinked when they saw the wonderful cakes. Were they real?

'It's *such* a pity, Mummy – I'd like to eat dozens of those cakes,' said Belinda, longingly, 'but when I've had one, I'm so full I can't eat any more. But American children can eat four or five at a time. I've seen them.'

'Well, I expect you enjoy your one as much as they enjoy their four or five,' said Mummy.

Another thing that the children found very strange was the number of people from many different cultures. Daddy said that because

America was a much newer country than Britain, people had come from lots of other countries to make her their home. It was so interesting. They made many new friends.

The woman who cleaned the corridor had twinkling eyes.

'You been up to the top of the Empire State, honey?' said the friendly old cleaner. 'Tell your Ma to take you along!'

And so one day Mummy and Daddy took them to the Empire State Building, the highest in New York. It was so high that Ann felt sure it really did touch the clouds.

Up they went in the lifts, shooting skywards so quickly that Ann clutched her tummy.

'What's the matter?' asked Daddy, smiling. 'Have you left your tummy behind?'

'It felt like it, when we suddenly shot up,'

said Ann. 'Oh Daddy – what a fast lift!'

The liftman spoke to them. 'Better look out for the pop in your ears now, sir,' he said. 'We're getting pretty high, and some people's ears go pop, and they feel funny. But it's nothing.'

Sure enough, their ears did go pop with a curious little noise in their ear drums. Ann felt a bit giddy, but it soon passed off.

They got into the last lift, to go up the top dozen or so floors. Up they went, and then, click! The door opened and they stepped out on top of the Empire State Building.

'OH!' cried Mike, in amazement. 'Mummy! We're right on the very top of the world!'

And really it did seem like it. Far, far below lay the earth, stretching out for miles and miles and miles all round the tower. An aeroplane flew by – below them! How

extraordinary! People down in the far-off
street were tiny dots – cars were smaller than
even Mike's dinky-ones at home.

'What a building!' said Daddy. 'What a

height! What a view!'

'We must be very near to Heaven up here,' said Ann, and the others smiled. Ann looked up as if she expected to see an angel or two around. But there was nothing but a few fleecy white clouds.

Then back they went down to earth again – down, down, down in the express lift, almost gasping at the way the lift seemed to fall down. Ann clutched her tummy again.

'I do like America,' said Belinda. 'It's full of the most wonderful things – it's *almost* magic!'

CHAPTER TWELVE
Time to go

Their time in America fled away fast. '*Every* thing goes fast in America; the taxis, the lifts, the parties – and even the time!' said Mike.

'Yes, no sooner is it morning than it seems to be night again,' said Belinda. 'I do really begin to wonder if time *is* different here – I mean, perhaps an hour isn't really an hour: perhaps it's only half an hour.'

'Oh, it's an hour all right,' said Mummy. 'It goes quickly because everything is strange and new and exciting, and the days go whizzing by.'

'I don't want to leave America,' said Ann. 'I like it.'

'Well, shall we leave you behind?' said Mummy. 'I've no doubt one of our American friends would love to keep a nice little girl like you.'

Ann looked alarmed. 'Oh *no!*' she said. 'It's just that I'm loving everything so much. I love England too. I couldn't *bear* not to go back.'

'I shan't mind going back at all,' said Mike. 'I love America and the Americans – but somehow they make me feel more English than ever, and they make me feel I belong to England. I want to get back to England, though I wouldn't mind staying a few weeks more here, Mummy.'

'Well, we've got our return tickets for home now,' said Mummy, 'and anyway we've very little money left to spend here. When the *Queen Elizabeth* docks in New York on

Wednesday, off we go in her, back home!'

The last day or two Mummy spent shopping with the children. They wanted to take little presents home for all their friends. The difficulty was what to take!

'There are so many things to choose from,' said Belinda, looking round a big store in despair. 'I just can't make up my mind. I mean, there are *thousands* of things here I'd like to take back. Don't Americans have a lot of everything, Mummy?'

'They do,' said Mummy, 'but then America is a rich country. She can afford to have everything.'

'Next time we come, don't let's stay in New York all the time,' said Belinda. 'Let's go and stay somewhere in the country, Mummy. I want to see what the trees and the flowers

are like – I've hardly seen a tree in New York!
And I've hardly seen a dog either.'

'Yes, it would be nice to stay somewhere
in the country,' said Mummy. 'After all, we
haven't really seen much of America if we
only stay in New York – any more than
Americans would see much of England if they
only stayed in London.'

'That's true,' said Belinda. 'England's
made up of a lot of things, isn't it, Mummy,
not just towns. It's – well, it's primroses in
springtime . . .'

'And taking the dogs for a long walk,' said
Mike.

'And sailing down the river,' said Daddy.

'And watching the first green blades come
through in the fields of corn,' said Mummy,
'and seeing all our lovely little patchwork of

fields, with their odd shapes and sizes.'

'It's Davey and Clopper the horses,' said Mike, remembering suddenly.

'And treading on the first patches of ice when we go to school in the winter,' said Belinda.

'Oh do stop,' said Ann. 'I'm getting so dreadfully homesick. How could we *ever* have left England?'

'It's good to travel,' said Daddy. 'We see how other people live and make themselves happy – and we love our own home and country all the more for seeing other people's. Each of us loves his own country best, and his own home best and his own family best.'

'When are we going to pack?' demanded Ann. 'I suddenly feel I want to. Oh Daddy – think how pleased Davey and Clopper will be to see us again!'

'I wonder if the caravans are all right,' said Mummy. 'I wonder if . . .'

'What a lot of home-birds you are, all of a sudden,' said Daddy, but he looked pleased. 'Well, the *Queen Elizabeth* sails at midnight tomorrow, so you can begin to pack as soon as you like.'

They packed – and dear me, Daddy had to go out and spend some of his last precious dollars on a new suitcase, because they had so many presents there just wasn't room to pack them all in!

'I shall carry Sadie, my walking doll,' said Belinda.

'Better put a bit of string on her, or buy her some toy reins, then,' said Mike. 'She might walk overboard!'

They said goodbye to all the friends they had made. They promised to come again for a longer stay. They took a last look at the wonderful lights on Broadway. And then they taxied to the *Queen Elizabeth*, which had now arrived once more and was down at the docks, waiting for them.

'There she is!' cried Mike, as he saw her enormous bows sticking up over the street. 'Good old Lizzie!'

'British, not American,' said Belinda, proudly. 'Britain is very tiny compared with America, isn't it, Mummy? But even a small country can do grand things!'

'Of course,' said Mummy. 'Now, here we are – up the gangway you go!'

And up they went, the girls clutching Josephine and Sadie, and Mike carrying his marvellous pistol. What a surprise when they got to their cabins!

Their American friends were generous to the last. Great sprays of flowers were there with friendly messages, boxes of magnificent roses, beautiful buttonholes to wear at dinner the next night, boxes of candies for the children!

'What a people!' said Daddy, as he looked at the enormous collection. 'I wonder we can bear to leave America, and go back to England!'

But the little island far away across the ocean, set in its own silver sea, was their home – the home they loved and wanted.

'Speed the ship!' said Daddy, as at last the *Elizabeth* began to move. 'Speed the ship home!'

'Home to England, dear old England,' chanted the children. 'Speed the ship, Captain, speed the ship!'

And away went the great ship, ploughing through the waves, eager to get back to England – it was her own home too!

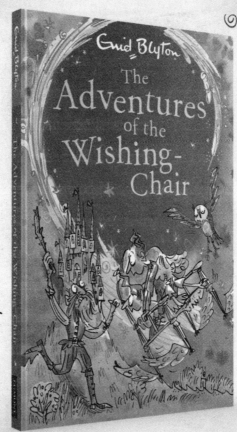

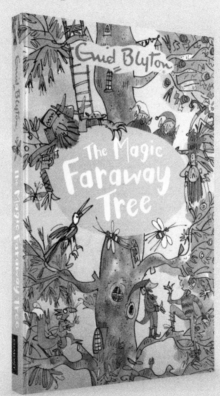